【美】南·沃克尔◎著
【美】MH.皮尔兹◎绘
范晓星◎译

天津出版传媒集团
新蕾出版社

献给布雷克、斯潘瑟、哈珀·凯斯林。

——南·沃克尔

献给艾迪。

——MH.皮尔兹

图书在版编目 (CIP) 数据

甜甜的糖果屋 / (美) 沃克尔 (Walker,N.) 著 ; (美) 皮尔兹 (Pilz,MH.) 绘 ; 范晓星译. -- 天津 : 新蕾出版社,2015.9(2024.12 重印)
(数学帮帮忙·互动版)
书名原文:The Yum-Yum House
ISBN 978-7-5307-6275-2

Ⅰ.①甜… Ⅱ.①沃… ②皮… ③范… Ⅲ.①数学-儿童读物 Ⅳ.①01-49

中国版本图书馆 CIP 数据核字(2015)第 223274 号

津图登字:02-2012-234

出版发行: 天津出版传媒集团
新蕾出版社
http://www.newbuds.com.cn
地　　址: 天津市和平区西康路 35 号(300051)
出 版 人: 马玉秀
电　　话: 总编办 (022)23332422
发行部 (022)23332679　23332351
传　　真: (022)23332422
经　　销: 全国新华书店
印　　刷: 天津新华印务有限公司
开　　本: 787mm×1092mm　1/16
印　　张: 3
版　　次: 2015 年 9 月第 1 版　2024 年 12 月第 20 次印刷
定　　价: 12.00 元

无处不在的数学

资深编辑　卢　江

人们常说“兴趣是最好的老师”，有了兴趣，学习就会变得轻松愉快。数学对于孩子来说或许有些难，因为比起语文，数学显得枯燥、抽象，不容易理解，孩子往往不那么喜欢。可许多家长都知道，学数学对于孩子的成长和今后的生活有多么重要。不仅数学知识很有用，学习数学过程中获得的数学思想和方法更会影响孩子的一生，因为数学素养是构成人基本素质的一个重要因素。但是，怎样才能让孩子对数学产生兴趣呢？怎样才能激发他们兴致勃勃地去探索数学问题呢？我认为，让孩子读些有趣的书或许是不错的选择。读了这套“数学帮帮忙”，我立刻产生了想把它们推荐给教师和家长朋友们的愿望，因为这真是一套会让孩子爱上数学的好书！

这套有趣的图书从美国引进，原出版者是美国资深教育专家。每本书讲述一个孩子们生活中的故事，由故事中出现的问题自然地引入一个数学知识，然后通过运用数学知识解决问题。比如，从帮助外婆整理散落的纽扣引出分类，从为小狗记录藏骨头的地点引出空间方位等等。故事素材全

部来源于孩子们的真实生活，不是童话，不是幻想，而是鲜活的生活实例。正是这些发生在孩子身边的故事，让孩子们懂得，数学无处不在并且非常有用；这些鲜活的实例也使得抽象的概念更易于理解，更容易激发孩子学习数学的兴趣，让他们逐渐爱上数学。这样的教育思想和方法与我国近年来提倡的数学教育理念是十分吻合的！

这是一套适合5~8岁孩子阅读的书，书中的有趣情节和生动的插画可以将抽象的数学问题直观化、形象化，为孩子的思维活动提供具体形象的支持。如果亲子共读的话，家长可以带领孩子推测情节的发展，探讨解决难题的办法，让孩子在愉悦的氛围中学到知识和方法。

值得教师和家长朋友们注意的是，在每本书的后面，出版者还加入了“互动课堂”及“互动练习”，一方面通过一些精心设计的活动让孩子巩固新学到的数学知识，进一步体会知识的含义和实际应用；另一方面帮助家长指导孩子阅读，体会故事中数学之外的道理，逐步提升孩子的阅读理解能力。

我相信孩子读过这套书后一定会明白，原来，数学不是烦恼，不是包袱，数学真能帮大忙！

“美味糖果屋！”格蕾丝说，“像姜饼屋，但是用了全麦饼干。这可是我一个人做的哟！”

我朝朋友威廉使了个眼色。

当然是她一个人做的，格蕾丝可是个手工达人。

去年夏天,我们街上的孩子们一起叠纸船。

格蕾丝叠的船有 7 张帆，我只折了一条有桨的船,还沉了底。

后来有一次我们举办街区舞会。

格蕾丝给小朋友们脸上画彩绘——蝴蝶、花朵，还有虎纹。

威廉和我负责宠物动物园。

宠物动物园只有一只动物，就是我的小狗萌萌。

起初这还算得上是个动物园，但狗狗一吃光饼干，就跑回家去了。

威廉和我去看格雷丝的美味糖果屋。“我用了 83 颗糖果！”格雷丝骄傲地说。

嗯，“美味糖果屋”这个名字真是名副其实呀！看一眼，就让人流口水。

“我们能尝一口吗？”我问道。

格雷丝笑着说：“麦琪，这可不是吃的哟！”

我们离开格蕾丝家时，我转身对威廉说：“咱们也能做一个美味糖果屋。”

威廉皱着眉头说：“你还记得上次你学格蕾丝给T恤衫染色的事吗？”

我耸耸肩说：“我怎么知道不能用水彩颜料呀？”

麦琪做美味糖果屋至少要 83 颗糖果，可麦琪现在一颗都没有。她还差多少颗？当然是 83 颗！想想看：
0 + 83 = 83

“这回可不一样。”我说，“全麦饼干、糖霜、糖果，怎么会出错呢？”

可威廉看上去还是不放心。

“走吧，威廉，”我说，“不就是 83 颗糖果吗？先从这些开始准备！我们要用这么多糖果，只就看一眼牙齿都受不了。”

在我家里，我们寻找各种需要的材料：饼干，有了；糖霜，有了；糖果，呃……

威廉看了一眼装糖果的碗。

"3颗柠檬糖？就这点儿？"

"我们可以去买一些。"我说。

"我一分钱也没有，你有吗？"

我摇摇头。

3 + □ = 83

麦琪有3颗糖。她需要买多少糖才能凑足83颗？想一想：你可以根据加法算式，列一个减法算式来找到答案：83 − 3 = 80。她还需要买80颗糖。

我们去了威廉家。威廉找到了一袋麦丽素。我把它们倒进碗里数了数，“15，16，17，威廉！”

“怎么啦？”威廉嘴里塞得鼓鼓的，说话咕哝咕哝的。

我再一数，只有 11 颗了！

11 + □ = 17

威廉吃了几颗麦丽素？想一想：17 − 11 = 6。他吃了 6 颗。

14 + □ = 83
他们需要买多少糖果?想一想:83 - 14 = 69。他们需要再买 69 颗糖果。

我们有 3 颗柠檬糖和 11 颗麦丽素,总共 14 颗糖果,离 83 颗还差得远呢。我们还要 69 颗糖果,才能跟格蕾丝用的糖果一样多!

“真糟糕,今天不是万圣节。”威廉说,“不然,我们就可以去要糖果了。”

“这个主意倒不赖……”我说。

我们按响了邓肯太太家的门铃。

“不穿万圣节的衣服去要糖果，我觉得怪傻的。”威廉抱怨道。

“不要把我们现在做的事想成是万圣节要糖果的事！”我说，“就把这件事当成是我们来借糖果。邓肯家总是有很多糖果。”

我告诉邓肯太太关于美味糖果屋的事。

“所以，我们需要很多糖果。”我解释道。

“哦，宝贝，我们两口子都在减肥呢。”她说，“我把家里所有的甜食都给处理了！”

看来想从邓肯家要到很多很多糖果是不可能了。

我们又去了贝林达小姐家碰运气。

“萌萌！”贝林达小姐一见到我家小狗就兴奋地叫道，“菲菲，你看，这是咱们的小朋友！”

菲菲低头看看我们家的萌萌，鄙视地抽了抽鼻子。

我问贝林达小姐家里有没有糖果。

贝林达小姐满脸笑容：“当然有了！”

贝林达小姐给了我们两大袋。

“好吃，看着就好吃。”威廉说着抓了一把扔进嘴里。

“啊！呸！呸！呸！”

“我觉得那是给萌萌的。”我说。

我把糖果又数了一遍，总共是 33 颗。还差 50 颗！除非我们把狗狗的饼干也算上。

我可不想加上狗狗的饼干。

33 + □ = 83

他们还需要多少颗糖果才能和格蕾丝用的数量相等呢？想一想：$83-33=50$。他们还需要 50 颗糖果。

接下来是弗洛先生家。

“咱们别去弗洛先生家了。”我建议。

“为什么？”威廉问,“他很和气呀！”

我提醒他，上次万圣节弗洛先生给我们的是黄豆做的零食。

威廉耸耸肩膀说:“味道还不赖，反正比狗饼干好吃。”

我们按响了门铃。

“您有泡泡糖吗？”我问弗洛先生。

“没有。”

“水果软糖呢？拐棍糖呢？”威廉问。

“孩子们，对不起，我不喜欢糖果。”

“只要是甜的都可以。”我跟他说。

弗洛先生笑了：“哦，如果是这样的话……”

弗洛先生拿出一袋东西给我们,里面是些棕色的皱巴巴的块状食品。

“这看起来真像是给狗狗吃的。”我说。

威廉往嘴里丢了一块,嚼了嚼,说:“好吃,你应该尝一块。”

我扔了一块香蕉干给萌萌。它闻了闻,然后把它丢在了地上。

我们向瑞兹太太家走去。

我们要时来运转啦。我能闻到糖果甜甜的味道了!

“请进!”瑞兹太太说,“我正在烤饼干呢。”

我们一边吃,一边告诉她关于美味糖果屋的事。她说,可以把剩下的巧克力送给我们。

莫瑞先生给我们一些用彩色纸包着的糖果。

我的临时保姆安波给了我们一些酸酸的虫虫糖。

连隔壁小托尼也给我们一根棒棒糖。

“威廉！他都舔过了！”

我让威廉把棒棒糖还给了托尼。

回到家，我们把糖果在桌子上摆开，我数了数，一共有75颗。

这已经是很多糖果了，但还是不到83颗。

这时，门铃响了。

75 + □ = 83

他们还需要多少颗糖果，才能和格蕾丝用的糖果一样多？想一想：83 − 75 = 8。他们还需要8颗糖果。

是邓肯先生来了。

啊！焦糖味奶糖、风车薄荷糖、玉米糖，还有迷你棉花糖。

“千万不要告诉邓肯太太，我减肥的时候作弊啦。”他说，“从现在起，我保证好好表现，什么糖果都不吃了！”

我数呀数，一直数到 150 颗糖果才停下来。

美味糖果宫殿就要做成啦！它将使格蕾丝的那个美味糖果屋看起来像是萌萌的狗窝。

我拿出饼干和糖霜，开始动手了。

可宫殿的墙怎么也粘不牢。

第一面墙倒向一侧。

第二面墙倒向了另一侧。

第三面墙全散了。

“我做不了！”我大声哭起来，“我做什么也永远不可能做得像格蕾丝那么好！”

“如果我们这样做呢？”威廉说道。他做了一个小小的房子给我看。虽然和我心里想象的完全不一样，但……这个小房子确实立起来了！

威廉粘上了一块香蕉干做烟囱。“看，这是弗洛先生的家。”

我大笑。

我试着照样做一个小房子，用巧克力豆做窗户。“这是瑞兹太太的家！”我说。

我们做了街上所有的房子，忙得都没注意到格雷丝已经到我家门口了。

格蕾丝盯着桌子看。

我们则盯着格蕾丝看。

然后，她笑了："一条美味糖果街？这个主意可真妙呀！"

我解释道:“我们原来想做一个大大的糖果屋,但墙总是没法固定。你是怎么做到的?”

“很简单!我先用硬纸板做成房子,然后把饼干粘在上面就好了。”

威廉和我你看看我,我看看你。

“纸板?!”他说。

“胶水?!”我叹息道。

“难怪你的美味糖果屋看上去更漂亮！”我说。

格蕾丝捏起一颗糖果，笑了：“也许我的糖果屋看上去更好看一些，但你们的更好吃呀！”

呵呵，她说得对！威廉和我做起东西来并不那么糟糕。只要我们全力以赴，谁知道我们能实现多么大的梦想呢？

趣味加减法

下面的应用题中，你能算出空格中的数字吗？

提示：加法和减法是有联系的，试试用加减法来找到答案。

例题：

格蕾丝做糖果屋要用 12 颗薄荷糖，可她现在只有 5 颗。

她还需要□颗。

我还需要几颗薄荷糖？

5 加几等于 12？ →加法：5+□=12

提示：可将算式转换成减法，算出答案。12−5=□

所以答案是 7。

格蕾丝还需要 7 颗薄荷糖！

1.贝林达小姐给麦琪一些狗狗饼干。

麦琪给小狗 5 块，还剩 10 块。

贝林达给麦琪□块狗狗饼干。

提示：□−5=10

我可以转换成加法来算出答案。

请转换成加法算式，看看答案应该是多少？

贝林达小姐给麦琪几块狗狗饼干？

2.威廉要用 50 颗糖豆来造糖果学校。

他已经有 65 颗糖豆了，剩下的他可以吃掉了！

威廉可以吃掉□颗糖豆。

提示：50+□=65

嗯，真好吃！

请转换成减法算式来算出答案。

威廉可以吃几颗糖豆？

答案：1.10+5=15（15 块饼干） 2.65−50=15（15 颗糖豆）

亲爱的家长朋友，请您和孩子一起完成下面这些内容，会有更大的收获哟！

提高阅读能力

- 阅读封面，让孩子猜想这会是一个怎样的故事。
- 读故事，验证孩子的猜想与故事吻合吗。
- 请读第3页和第6页，糖果屋和姜饼屋有什么不同？格蕾丝用了多少块糖果？
- 威廉发现小狗骨头形状的饼干其实是什么？
- 麦琪和威廉为什么造了一条糖果街？

互动课堂

巩固数学概念

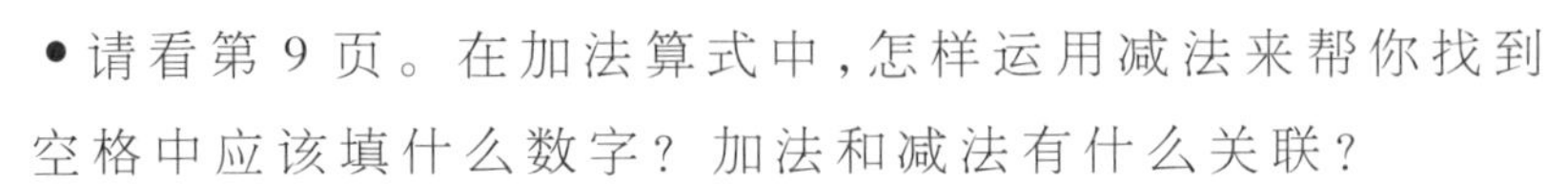

- 请看第 9 页。在加法算式中，怎样运用减法来帮你找到空格中应该填什么数字？加法和减法有什么关联？
- 请看第 16 页和第 22 页，然后用第 9 页上的方法来计算答案。
- 假设格蕾丝和麦琪想做一个美味糖果屋，一共需要 36 块全麦饼干，但他们现在只有 16 块，他们还需要多少块呢？请列出算式，找到答案。

- 假设瑞兹太太有 98 颗巧克力豆，她做完饼干后剩下 48 颗，她用掉了几颗？98 − □ = 48

生活中的数学

- 拿一盒乒乓球放在孩子面前，家长取出 4 个乒乓球，盒子里还剩 8 个乒乓球，盒里原来有多少乒乓球呢？
- 和孩子一起去超市购物，让小朋友开动脑筋，想一想购物中会有哪些环节要用到加减法呢？

今天是麦琪的生日，我有 100 元钱，想从下面的礼物中选取两件送给她，我有几种选法？每种选法需要多少钱？还剩多少钱？

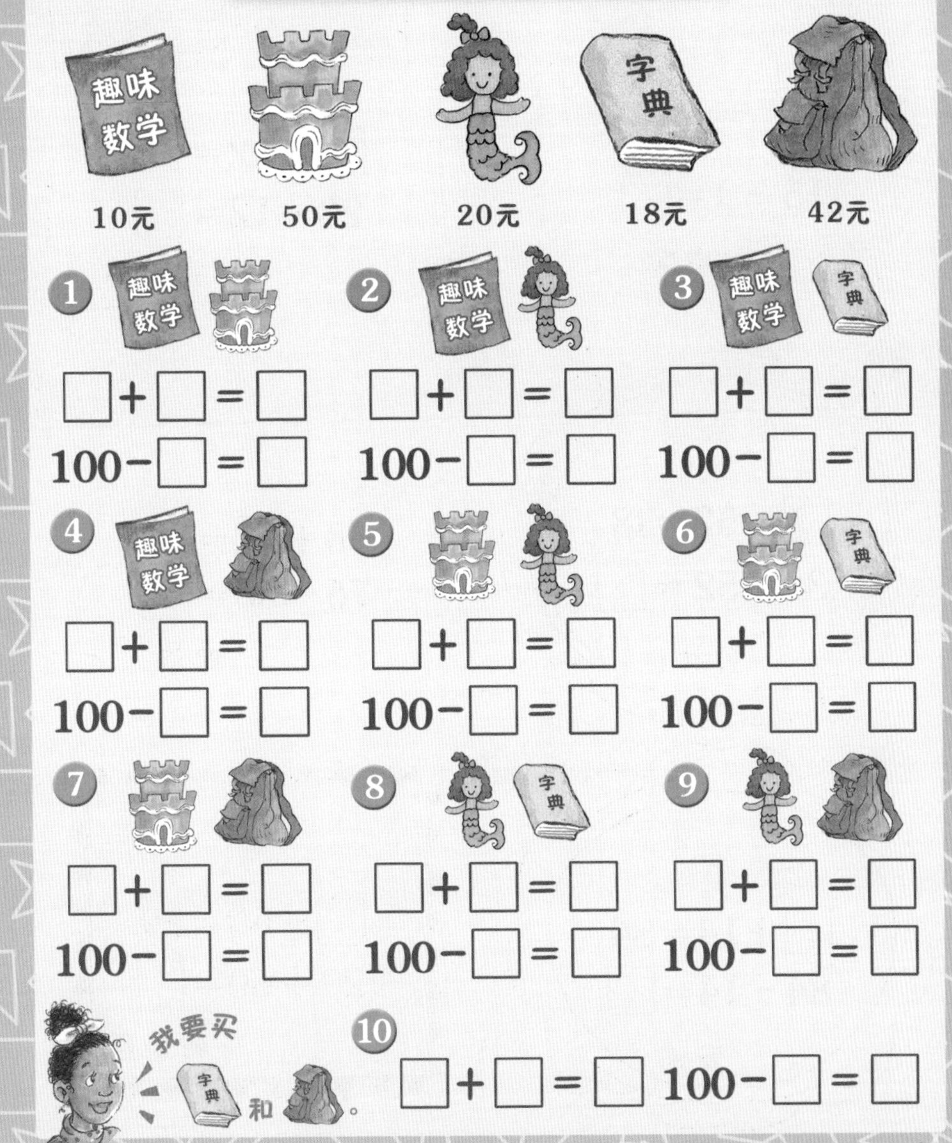

互动练习2

麦琪的好友们也纷纷送来祝福。他们还在贺卡上附上了一道算术题。快来帮助麦琪完成这些有趣的数字贺卡吧！

1

祝麦琪
生日快乐！

$9+\square=15$

$15-9=\square$

威廉

2

愿麦琪永远开心！

$\square-12=23$

$23+12=\square$

邓肯太太

3

愿麦琪
学习进步！

$\square-52=38$

$38+52=\square$

贝林达

4

愿麦琪
越长越漂亮！

$50+\square=76$

$76-50=\square$

弗洛

5

愿麦琪
心想事成！

$\square+14=84$

$84-14=\square$

安波

6

愿我们成为
一辈子的好友！

$\square-60=29$

$29+60=\square$

格蕾丝

提示：每题下一行的算式都是上一行的算式通过加减法的转换得出来的。

互动练习3

爸爸和妈妈亲手为麦琪做了一个生日蛋糕，一共买来15根蜡烛，剩下6根，你能帮忙算算用了多少根吗？

威廉还为麦琪精心做了她想要的糖果屋。他一共买来90颗糖豆，用去了16颗红色的糖豆、13颗蓝色的糖豆、20颗黄色的糖豆、10颗绿色的糖豆、14颗紫色的糖豆、6颗橘色的糖豆。

根据上述信息，回答下面的问题。

1 一共用去了多少颗红色糖豆和蓝色糖豆？

□○□=□

2 一共用去了多少颗黄色糖豆和绿色糖豆？

□○□=□

3 一共用去了多少颗紫色糖豆和橘色糖豆？

□○□=□

4 一共用去了多少颗糖豆？

□○□○□=□

5 剩下的糖豆被威廉吃掉了，他吃了多少颗？

□○□=□

互动练习4

我和麦琪、威廉要去动物园玩。瞧，马路上的车可真多呀！只有算对车身上的题，我们才能顺利到达动物园。快来帮我们算一算吧！

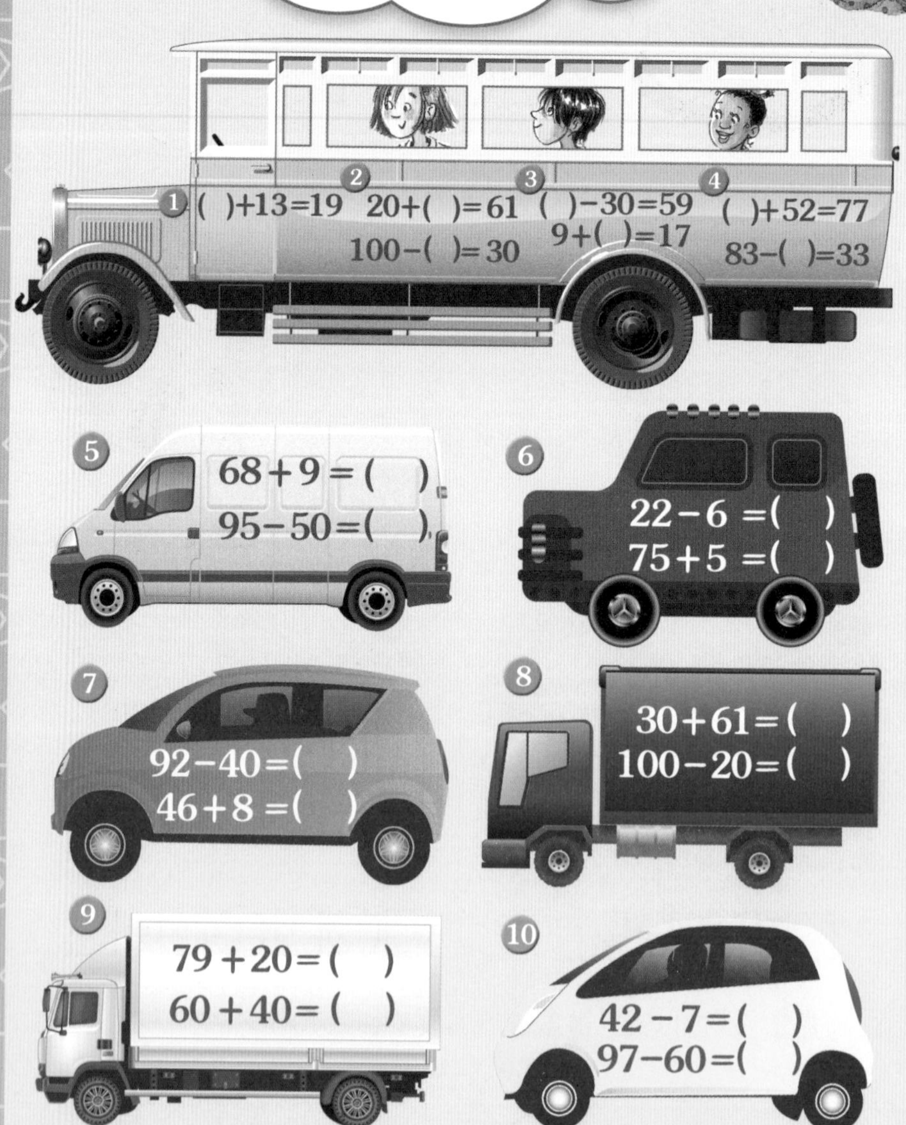

动物园到了。根据各种小动物给出的信息，快来完成下面的计算吧！

小猴有 30 只。

小狮子有 8 只。

小兔有 48 只。

小羊比小兔多 7 只。

小熊比小猴少 10 只。

1. 小羊有多少只？

□○□=□

2. 小熊有多少只？

□○□=□

3. 小兔比小狮子多多少只？

□○□=□

4. 小熊比小羊少多少只？

□○□=□

5. 小狮子比小猴少多少只？

□○□=□

6. 小羊比小猴多多少只？

□○□=□

小动物们迷路了。房屋前的数字牌分别是小动物们手中各自算术题的结果，只要将对应的算式连接起来就能帮他们找到家哟！

小朋友，你能分步计算出下列题目吗？请将分步结果，填入下图的空白处。

互动练习7

威廉和好朋友办了一个家庭图书馆，现在他们一共有 96 本图画书，第一周借出了 28 本，第二周借出了 30 本，现在图书馆里还有多少本书呢？

让我们和小刺猬一起玩儿扎苹果的游戏吧。3 只小刺猬分别设置了不同的条件，之后将每个苹果的运算结果与对应的条件连接起来。

互动练习 1:

一共有 10 种选法

①10+50=60　②10+20=30

100−60=40　100−30=70

③10+18=28　④10+42=52

100−28=72　100−52=48

⑤50+20=70　⑥50+18=68

100−70=30　100−68=32

⑦50+42=92　⑧20+18=38

100−92=8　100−38=62

⑨20+42=62　⑩18+42=60

100−62=38　100−60=40

互动练习 2:

①6、6　②35、35　③90、90

④26、26⑤70、70　⑥89、89

互动练习 3:

15−6=9

①16+13=29　②20+10=30

③14+6=20　④29+30+20=79

⑤90−79=11

互动练习 4:

①6　②41、70　③89、8

④25、50　⑤77、45　⑥16、80

⑦52、54　⑧91、80　⑨99、100

⑩35、37

互动练习 5:

①48+7=55　②30−10=20

③48−8=40　④55−20=35

⑤30−8=22　⑥55−30=25

互动练习 6:

①76、36、23　②34、26、16

③50、41、21

互动练习 7:

38 本

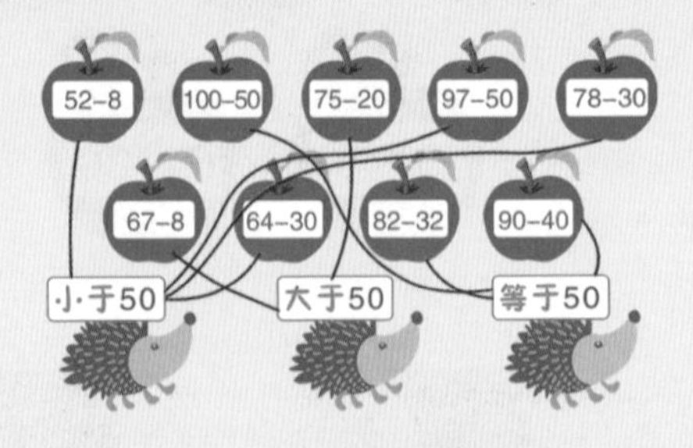

（习题设计：董惠平　鹿　美）

THE YUM-YUM HOUSE

"It's a yum-yum house!" Grace says. "Like a gingerbread house, but with graham crackers. I made it myself." I roll my eyes at my friend William.

Of course she made it herself. Grace is the queen of making things herself.

Last summer all the kids on our street made paper boats.

Grace made a ship with seven sails.

I made a rowboat—and it sank.

Then there was the block party.

Grace did face painting—butterflies, flowers, tiger stripes.

William and I ran a petting zoo.

The zoo had one animal — my dog, Homer.

At least, it did until the dog biscuits ran out. Then Homer went home.

William and I check out the yum-yum house. "I used 83 pieces of candy," Grace says proudly.

Mmm. Yum-yum is right. Just looking at it makes me drool.

"Can we have a taste?" I ask.

She giggles. "It's not for eating, Maggie!"

I turn to William as we leave. "We could do that. We could make a yum-yum house."

He frowns. "Remember when you tried to paint a T-shirt like Grace did?"

I shrug. "How was I supposed to know that watercolors wouldn't work?"

"This is different," I say. "Graham crackers. Frosting. Candy. What can go wrong?"

He still doesn't look sure.

"Come on, William," I say. "Eighty-three pieces of candy? That's just a start! We'll use so much candy, our teeth will hurt just looking at it."

At my house we search for the things we need. Graham crackers—check. Frosting—check. Candy... uh-oh.

William peers into the candy bowl. "Three lemon drops? That's it?"

"We could buy more," I say.

"I don't have any money. Do you?"

I shake my head.

We go to William's house. He finds an open bag of malted milk balls. I dump it out to count. "15, 16, 17—William!"

"Wha?" he mumbles, his mouth full.

I count again. Only 11 left!

So, we have 3 lemon drops and 11 malted milk balls.

That's 14 candies — a long way from 83. We need 69 more candies just to tie Grace!

"Too bad it isn't Halloween," William says. "We could go trick-or-treating."

"That's not a bad idea..." I say.

We ring the Duncans' doorbell.

"I feel silly trick-or-treating without costumes," William complains.

"Don't think of it as trick-or-treating," I say. "Think of it as borrowing. The Duncans always have a ton of candy."

I tell Mrs. Duncan about the yum-yum house. "So we need lots of candy," I explain.

"Oh, honey, we've gone on a diet," she says. "I got rid of every sweet treat in the house!"

So much for getting a ton of candy.

We try Miss Belinda next.

"Homer!" she trills when she sees my dog. "Look, Fifi! It's our little friend!"

Fifi looks down at Homer and sniffs.

I ask Miss Belinda about candy.

She beams. "Of course I have some!"

She gives us two bags.

"Yum! These look good," William says.

He tosses a handful in his mouth.

"Bleeeeccccchh!"

"I think that bag was for Homer," I say.

I count up the people candies. Our

new grand total is 33. We're still 50 behind Grace! Unless we count the doggie treats.

I really don't want to count the doggie treats.

Floyd's house is next.

"Let's skip Floyd's house," I say.

"Why?" William asks. "He's nice!"

I remind him about the soybean snacks Floyd gave out on Halloween.

William shrugs. "They weren't so terrible. Better than doggie treats."

We ring the doorbell.

"Do you have any gumdrops?" I ask Floyd.

"Nope."

"Jelly beans? Candy canes?" William asks.

"Sorry, dude. Candy isn't my scene."

"We'll take anything sweet!" I tell him.

He smiles. "Well, in that case..."

I stare at the brown, wrinkly lumps Floyd gave us. "Now, these look like they're meant for dogs," I say.

William pops one in his mouth and chews. "Yum. You should try one."

I toss a piece of the dried banana to Homer. He sniffs it, then leaves it on the ground.

We head for Mrs. Rizzuto's. Our luck is about to change. I can smell it!

"Come in!" she says. "I'm baking cookies."

While we eat, we tell her about the yum-yum house. She says we can have her extra chocolate chips.

Mr. Mori gives us little candies wrapped in colored paper.

My babysitter, Amber, gives us sour worms.

Even little Tony next door hands us a lollipop.

"William! He's licked it!"

I make William give it back.

Back home, we spread the candy out on the table. I count 75 pieces.

That's a lot of candy. But it's less than 83.

Just then, the doorbell rings.

It's Mr. Duncan.

Wow! Caramel creams. Pinwheel mints. Candy corn. Mini marshmallows.

"Please don't tell Mrs. Duncan I've been cheating on our diet," he says. "From now on, I'm going to be good!"

I stop counting candies when I hit

150.

This is going to be a yum-yum palace! It will make Grace's yum-yum house look like Homer's doghouse.

I get out the graham crackers and frosting, and we get to work.

My first wall falls over to one side.

My second wall falls over to the other side.

My third wall just falls apart.

"I can't do this!" I wail. "I'll never do anything as well as Grace!"

"What if we do it this way?" William says.

He shows me a tiny house. It's not what I had in mind at all. But...it does stay up!

He sticks on a chunk of dried banana for the chimney. "Look. It's Floyd's house."

I laugh.

I try building a little house like his. I make the windows out of chocolate chips.

"It's Mrs. Rizzuto's house!" I say.

We make all the houses on our street.

We're so busy, we don't even notice Grace coming to the door.

Grace stares at the table.

We stare at Grace.

Then she smiles. "A whole yum-yum street! What a great idea!"

I explain. "We wanted to make one big house, but we couldn't get the walls to stay up. How did you do it?"

"Easy! I made the house out of cardboard. Then I glued on the graham crackers."

William and I look at each other.

"Cardboard," he says.

"Glue," I moan.

"No wonder your yum-yum house looks so much nicer," I say.

Grace nibbles a piece of candy and smiles. "Maybe mine looks prettier... but yours is yummier!"

You know, she's right! William and I aren't so bad at making things.

If we really put our minds to it—who knows what we could do?